Ask for May,
Settle for June

*Doonesbury books by G. B. Trudeau
published by New English Library*

**IN SEARCH OF REAGAN'S BRAIN
ASK FOR MAY, SETTLE FOR JUNE**

a Doonesbury book by

GB Trudeau.

Ask for May, Settle for June

NEW ENGLISH LIBRARY

First published in the USA in 1982 by Holt, Rinehart and Winston

The cartoons in this book have appeared in newspapers in
the United States and abroad under the auspices of Universal Press Syndicate.

First NEL Paperback Edition October 1983

NEL Books are published by
New English Library,
Mill Road, Dunton Green,
Sevenoaks, Kent.
Editorial office: 47 Bedford Square, London WC1B 3DP

Made and printed in Great Britain by
Hazell Watson & Viney Ltd, Aylesbury, Bucks

British Library Cataloguing in Publication Data

Trudeau, G.B.
  Ask for May, settle for June.—(Doonesbury; 2)
  I. Title   II. Series
  741.5′973

  ISBN 0-450-05521-3

GENERAL HAIG, I WONDER IF WE MIGHT TURN OUR ATTENTION NOW TO THE QUESTION OF THE NIXON PARDON.

ACCORDING TO PUBLISHED ACCOUNTS, YOU DISCUSSED THE PARDON WITH MR. FORD ON AUGUST 1, 1974, AGAIN LATER THAT NIGHT, AND ONCE MORE ON AUGUST 2. CORRECT?

YES, BUT THERE WAS NEVER ACTUALLY A QUID PRO QUO OFFER. I WAS SIMPLY DESCRIBING ONE POSSIBLE SCENARIO.

AND MR. FORD'S REACTION? HE WAS APPALLED ALL THREE TIMES.

OKAY, PEOPLE,
QUIET ON THE
SET, PLEASE!

SCENE ONE...
TAKE ONE!

"MR. REAGAN GOES
TO WASHINGTON"

1 SC... 1 TAKE

ACTION!

GBTrudeau

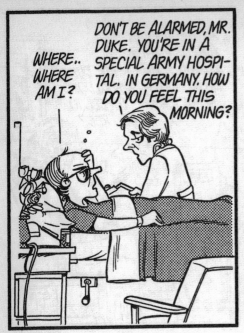

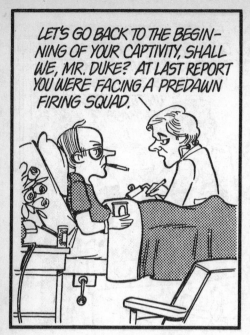

LET'S GO BACK TO THE BEGINNING OF YOUR CAPTIVITY, SHALL WE, MR. DUKE? AT LAST REPORT YOU WERE FACING A PREDAWN FIRING SQUAD.

RIGHT. AT THAT POINT, NEGOTIATIONS HAD KIND OF BOGGED DOWN. I WAS FORCED TO MAKE A LAST-DITCH OFFER OF $250,000, WHICH IT TURNED OUT WAS THE GOING RATE FOR A STAY OF EXECUTION.

IT WAS AN INCREDIBLE RIP-OFF, BUT I FIGURED, WHAT THE HELL, I'D BE LONG GONE BY THE TIME MY CHECK BOUNCED. UNFORTUNATELY, THEY LOCKED ME UP IN A HOTEL AS INSURANCE.

OKAY, BALD ONE, BACK TO THE ROOF.

I CAN'T UNDERSTAND IT. THEY MUST HAVE FROZEN MY ASSETS.

GBTrudeau

ACTUALLY, DOC, LOOKING BACK ON IT NOW, I THINK THE WORST PART OF THE WHOLE ORDEAL WAS THE EXCRUCIATING BOREDOM..

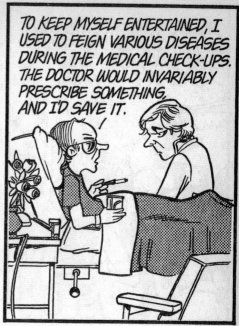

TO KEEP MYSELF ENTERTAINED, I USED TO FEIGN VARIOUS DISEASES DURING THE MEDICAL CHECK-UPS. THE DOCTOR WOULD INVARIABLY PRESCRIBE SOMETHING, AND I'D SAVE IT.

THEN, EVERY SIX WEEKS OR SO, I'D HAVE A PARTY. IT NEVER FAILED TO SCARE THE HELL OUT OF THE GUARDS.

GBTrudeau

IS HE DEAD?

I DON'T THINK SO. HE JUST GIGGLED.

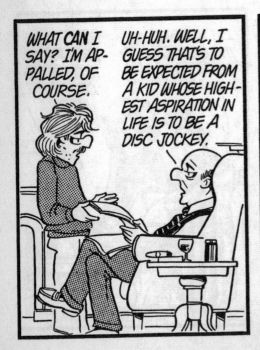

GOOD EVENING. TODAY THE FUROR CONTINUED OVER PRESIDENT REAGAN'S RECENT STATEMENT THAT THE ONLY LESSON OF VIETNAM WAS TO "NEVER ENTER INTO A WAR YOU DON'T INTEND TO WIN."

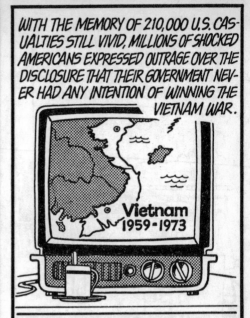

WITH THE MEMORY OF 210,000 U.S. CASUALTIES STILL VIVID, MILLIONS OF SHOCKED AMERICANS EXPRESSED OUTRAGE OVER THE DISCLOSURE THAT THEIR GOVERNMENT NEVER HAD ANY INTENTION OF WINNING THE VIETNAM WAR.

Vietnam
1959-1973

I'M ROLAND HEDLEY. AS CRIES OF "NEVER AGAIN" RING OUT ACROSS THE COUNTRY TONIGHT, JOIN ME AS WE TAKE A LOOK INTO OUR OWN FRONT YARD.. FOR *A WAR WE CAN WIN!*

BROUGHT TO YOU BY HERTZ, WHERE THE WINNERS RENT..

EL SALVADOR

ONE FOR THE GIPPER 1981-?

GBTrudeau

IN THE WAKE OF MR. REAGAN'S STARTLING DISCLOSURE THAT THE U.S. NEVER INTENDED TO WIN THE VIETNAM WAR, SCORES OF VETERANS HAVE COME FORWARD TO CONFIRM HIS CLAIM. SGT. LENNY McCOVEY RECALLS.

I REMEMBER ONCE NEAR DA NANG, WE HAD THIS GOOK UNIT PINNED DOWN IN THE OPEN. WE WERE ABOUT TO CALL IN SOME SKY-RAIDERS FOR A NAPALM DROP WHEN THE C.O. JUST CALLED OFF THE OPERATION.

DID THAT HAPPEN OFTEN?

HELL, YES. EVERY TIME WE HAD A REAL CHANCE OF STICKING IT TO CHARLIE, WORD WOULD COME DOWN THE U.S. WASN'T SERIOUS ABOUT WINNING IN VIETNAM.

INCREDIBLE. HOW MANY OTHER G.I's KNEW ABOUT THIS?

PRETTY MUCH ALL 500,000 OF US.

GB Trudeau

WHETHER THE U.S. MEANT TO WIN THE VIETNAM WAR OR NOT, TODAY THERE IS GROWING PRESSURE TO FIND A WAR WE CAN WIN. U.S. STRATEGIST ABE LEVIN EXPLAINS HOW EL SALVADOR WAS SELECTED.

IT WASN'T EASY. WE'D BEEN LOOKING FOR A PLACE TO DRAW THE LINE FOR WEEKS, BUT THERE JUST WEREN'T ANY CIVIL WARS ON THE FRONT PAGE. FINALLY, SOME GUY IN RESEARCH HIT ON EL SALVADOR.

IT WAS PERFECT. SMALL, CLOSE TO HOME, AND THE RIGHT SIDE WAS ALREADY WINNING. WE HIT IT HARD. WITHIN DAYS, WE'D TURNED EL SALVADOR INTO A METAPHOR FOR THE GEOPOLITICAL STRUGGLE BETWEEN THE SUPERPOWERS!

AND THE RUSSIANS AGREED WITH YOUR CHOICE?

WELL, NO, THEY WANTED SOME PERSIAN GULF STATE, BUT WE PUT OUR FOOT DOWN.

GBTrudeau

GOOD EVENING. TODAY THE STATE DEPARTMENT FINALLY CONCEDED THAT ITS HIGHLY ACCLAIMED "WHITE PAPER" ON SOVIET INTERFERENCE IN EL SALVADOR WAS RIDDLED WITH ERRORS AND MISLEADING STATEMENTS.

THE WHITE PAPER, SUBTITLED "SHAFIK: PORTRAIT OF A COMMUNIST," HAD BEEN WIDELY USED BY OFFICIALS TO DEFEND U.S. MILITARY AID TO THE REPRESSIVE REGIME OF JOSÉ DUARTE.

TODAY, SECRETARY OF STATE HAIG ACCEPTED FULL RESPONSIBILITY FOR THE FRAUDULENT REPORT, ADMITTING THAT HE AND OTHER TRUSTING OFFICIALS HAD BEEN DUPED BY THE REPORT'S YOUNG AUTHOR, JON D. GLASSMAN.

SAID A SHAKEN HAIG, "DISGRACEWISE, THIS IS A DIRECT HIT."

G.B. Trudeau

THE EL SALVADOR "WHITE PAPER." ONCE A TEXTBOOK CASE OF INDIRECT ARMED AGGRESSION BY COMMUNIST POWERS, NOW A DISCREDITED DOCUMENT, SHROUDED IN SHAME.

DID THE COMMUNIST LEADER "SHAFIK" DESCRIBED IN THE WHITE PAPER EVEN EXIST? WE PUT THE QUESTION TO THE REPORT'S AUTHOR, JON GLASSMAN, WHO AGREED TO TALK ONLY IN SILHOUETTE.

OF COURSE, "SHAFIK" EXISTS. IT'S JUST THAT THE EVIDENCE OF HIS ACTIVITIES IS INCONCLUSIVE. BUT IF "SHAFIK" DIDN'T INVITE SOVIET INTERFERENCE IN EL SALVADOR, THEN OTHERS JUST LIKE HIM DID.

THEN "SHAFIK" IS, IN EFFECT, A COMPOSITE COMMUNIST?

RIGHT. I JUST DIDN'T WANT TO BREAK UP THE FLOW OF THE STORY.

WHY DIDN'T THE STATE DEPARTMENT CATCH THE GLARING ERRORS AND FABRICATIONS OF THE EL SALVADOR "WHITE PAPER"? FOGGY BOTTOM TOPSIDER ED FROST EXPLAINS..

LOOK, WHEN I FIRST READ "SHAFIK: PORTRAIT OF A COMMUNIST," I WAS SKEPTICAL MYSELF. IT SEEMED TOO PAT. BUT THE WRITER WAS ONE OF OUR STAR BUREAUCRATS. WE TRUSTED HIM.

I SUPPOSE WE SHOULD HAVE BEEN MORE ALERT. I SUPPOSE WE SHOULD HAVE TRIED TO CONFIRM THE EXISTENCE OF "SHAFIK" AND DETERMINE WHETHER HE WAS SOVIET-DOMINATED..

WHY DIDN'T YOU?

WELL, WE FELT IT MIGHT PLACE HIS LIFE IN JEOPARDY.

SECRETARY HAIG, WILL YOU BE REVIEWING OTHER STATE DEPARTMENT WHITE PAPERS AS A RESULT OF THE SCANDAL?

NEGATIVE. THERE WILL BE NO INTERDICTION OF COMMUNIQUES WHICH IMPACT ON OUR STRATEGY IN THE LATIN AMERICAN SECTOR. WE'RE NOT GOING TO ABORT THE WHOLE SHOOTING MATCH OVER ONE ROTTEN APPLE!

UNTIL WE'VE DAMAGE-ASSESSED OUR POSITION, THOUGH, WE WILL BE RED-LIGHTING CURRENT U.S. CONTAINMENT OF LOCAL LEFTIST ELEMENTS IN COSTA RICA, GUATEMALA AND — COLOMBIA.

WHAT ABOUT FRANCE?

THAT'S ALREADY BEEN CANCELLED. WE FEEL THE SITUATION IN PARIS HAS STABILIZED.